Chen's Christmas Tree

by Michèle Dufresne

Pioneer Valley Educational Press, Inc.

Mom said, "Let's go and get a Christmas tree."

"Yes," said Chen.
"Let's get a big, big tree."

"Go and get the saw,"
said Mom.

Chen went and got the saw.
"Let's go," he said.

Chen and Mom
got in the car and went to
the Christmas tree farm.

"Look, Mom. Here is a good tree," said Chen. "Let's get this tree."

"That tree is too big," said Mom. "It will not fit in the house!"

"Oh," said Chen.

"Here, Mom.
I like this tree," said Chen.

"Chen, that tree is too big,"
said Mom.
"It will not fit in the house!"

"Oh," said Chen.

"Here is a good tree.
I like this tree," said Chen.

"Yes," said Mom.
"This is a good tree.
It will fit in the house."

Chen and Mom cut down the tree.

They took the tree to the car.

"Mom, this is a good tree," said Chen.
"It will fit in the house, but it will not fit in the car!"